The Tokyo Puzzles

2 / Reducing Squares

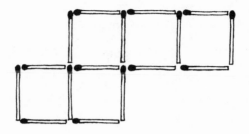

Form five squares with sixteen matches, as in the illustration. Change the positions of two matches so that there will be only four squares of the same size.

1 / A Cherry and a Glass

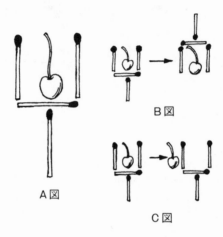

B 図

A 図

C 図

Let's begin with a clever match puzzle. Form a cocktail glass with four matches, as shown in Figure A. Now change the positions of two matches—and only two—so that the cherry lies outside the glass. The glass may lie upside down or sideways, as long as its size and shape remain the same.

Figure B shows how two matches can be moved, but the cherry remains in the glass. In Figure C the glass is empty, but three matches have changed positions. Therefore, neither B nor C is the solution.

PUZZLES

well-suited in difficulty to the sophistication of the student, third, to answer questions, and finally, if the teacher is capable of it, to give an occasional word of inspiration."

If you hated math in school, it wasn't because the subject is dreary but because you had dreary teachers who in turn also disliked mathematics. Mr. Fujimura is not a dreary teacher.

MARTIN GARDNER

sons), all married, who have provided him with seven grandchildren. Among intellectual games, his chief enthusiasms are *go* and *shogi* (Japanese chess). Sam Loyd, the American puzzle genius, created hundreds of beautiful chess problems. Mr. Fujimura has created similar problems for Japanese chess and *go*. One must, of course, play those games to appreciate them, so they are not well known outside of Japan.

The book you now hold is a translation of Mr. Fujimura's latest book, *Puzzles, Puzzles, Puzzles*. These are for the most part problems that he has selected from the vast literature of classic puzzles, retelling them with his own story lines and in many cases giving them fresh angles. Many of these classics are better known in Japan than here and are likely to be unfamiliar to the average reader. Some puzzles in the book are original. The illustrations, reproduced from the Japanese edition, are by Y. Kato. Where there are sequences of small drawings they have been altered to go from left to right rather than right to left.

Please do not suppose that the only function of puzzles is to entertain. Puzzles are a way of teaching mathematics. Indeed, they are the best way to teach it. Fred Hoyle, the famous British astronomer, taught mathematics at Cambridge University for twenty years. In his recent book *Ten Faces of the Universe* he states in strong terms his belief that mathematics should never be *taught* at all. Students must learn for themselves. How?

"By solving puzzles. The functions of the teacher should be, first, to select in a wise way the material on which the puzzles are based, second, to make sure the puzzles are to a high school mathematics journal published by the well-known Tokyo firm of Kenkyu-sha. The same firm published his first three books: *Modern Mathematical Puzzles* (1938), *100 New Mathematical Puzzles* (1940), and *A Study of Mathematical Puzzles* (1943).

After the Second World War, Mr. Fujimura found life difficult and was "compelled," as he put it, to become a high school teacher of mathematics, first at a public school, then at a private one. He continued teaching until his retirement in 1972. Throughout this period he continued to write books on puzzles and to contribute to newspapers and magazines. Oyama-shoten published his *Mathematical Puzzles* in 1955. This was followed by two books of entirely original logic problems: *Reasoning Puzzles,* volumes 1 and 2 (1955, 1956). They became national best-sellers.

The great success of *Reasoning Puzzles* turned Mr. Fujimura into a well-known public figure. He was very much in demand as a lecturer and as a guest on radio and TV talk shows. In 1959 he had his own weekly TV puzzle show.

And of course he continued to turn out books. Diamond Press issued his *New Puzzles* (1957), *Invitation to Puzzles* (1963), *Puzzles and Problems* (1969), and expanded versions of his *Reasoning Puzzles* (1969, 1970). These were followed with *Dialogue on Puzzles* (1971), *Puzzles and Thinking* (1973), *Origin of Puzzles* (1975), and *Puzzles, Puzzles, Puzzles* (1976). In addition, Mr. Fujimura is the author of several puzzle books for children and the translator of two books by the Canadian puzzle maker J. A. H. Hunter.

Mr. Fujimura has five children (two daughters, three

Introduction

Kobon Fujimura is Japan's leading maker of puzzles and writer of popular puzzle books. I have not had the honor of meeting him, but I have met his attractive daughter and her husband when they were in the States a few years ago, and Mr. Fujimura and I have exchanged so many letters that I feel we are old friends.

In addition to our fondness for recreational mathematics, we also share an unbounded admiration for the great English puzzle expert Henry E. Dudeney. It was a book by Dudeney that first aroused Mr. Fujimura's interest in puzzles. He was then a young man attending the Nagoya College of Commerce. One of his "treasures," as he calls it, is a letter that Dudeney sent him dated December 24, 1926. "It is my passport," he writes, "to the land of puzzle making." Mr. Fujimura is the translator into Japanese of Dudeney's *Amusements in Mathematics* as well as Dudeney's *536 Puzzles and Curious Problems*, a merging of two of Dudeney's later puzzle books that Scribners published in 1969 and that I had the pleasure of editing.

Kobon Fujimura was born in 1903 in Osaka, Japan. After leaving college, he and his brother took over the management of his father's curiosity shop in Osaka. Puzzles are, of course, curiosities of the mind, so the day-to-day chores in the shop and the hobby of recreational mathematics went well together.

From 1932 until 1944 Mr. Fujimura contributed puzzles

Contents

English language translation and introduction copyright
© 1978 Charles Scribner's Sons. Original Japanese
language versions copyright © 1976, 1970, 1969 by
Kozaburo Fujimura. Original Japanese language
versions published by Diamond Inc., Tokyo.

Library of Congress Cataloging in Publication Data

Fujimura, Kozaburo, Date
    The Tokyo puzzles.

    Translation of Pazuru pazuru pazuru.
    1. Mathematical recreations.   I. Gardner, Martin,
Date.   II. Title.
QA95.F8213   793.7'4   77-26661
ISBN 0-684-15536-2
ISBN 0-684-15537-0 pbk

1 3 5 7 9 11 13 15 17 19 V/C 20 18 16 14 12 10 8 6 4 2
1 3 5 7 9 11 13 15 17 19 V/P 20 18 16 14 12 10 8 6 4 2

Printed in the United States of America

The
Tokyo Puzzles

Kobon Fujimura

Edited and with an Introduction
by Martin Gardner

Translated by Fumie Adachi

Charles Scribner's Sons NEW YORK

3 / Reducing Triangles

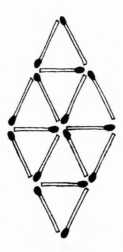

As illustrated, form eight equilateral triangles with sixteen matches. Remove four matches so as to leave just four triangles of the same size, with no loose ends.

4 / A Match Dog

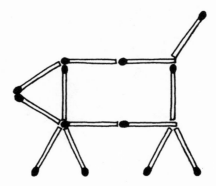

This dog, made of matches, is here shown facing west. Make him face east by changing the positions of just two matches. It is easily done by moving three matches, but can you do it by moving only two?

5 / Tropical Fish

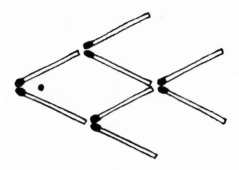

A tropical fish is swimming in a tank. The fish faces west. Make it face east by changing the positions of three matches.

6 / Three Times as Big

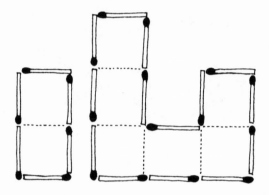

Arrange twenty matches to make two figures, as shown in the illustration. One figure uses six matches, the other fourteen. You can see from the dotted lines that one figure has an area three times the size of the other.

Transfer one match from the larger figure to the smaller one so that the small figure now has seven matches and the larger thirteen. Then rearrange eight matches to make the large figure once again three times as big as the other. Do not put two matches side by side or leave any part of the border open.

7 / Vanishing Squares

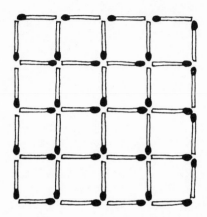

Arrange forty matches as shown in the illustration. Then check the number of squares, which in some cases may overlap one another. We find sixteen small squares, nine medium squares, four large squares, and one square enclosing all the others. There are thirty in all.

Now remove nine matches so that no square of any size remains.

8 / Touching Matches

Arrange six matches so that each match touches all the others.

9 / Seven
Matches Will Do

"Seven matches can do the same trick," Gardner says in his *Mathematical Puzzles and Diversions*. Using seven matches instead of six, solve problem number 8.

10 / Hexagon to Parallelogram

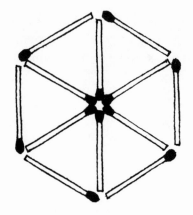

Arrange twelve matches in a hexagon as shown. Within the hexagon there are six parallelograms.

Now change the positions of four matches and make twelve parallelograms of various sizes. They may overlap.

11 / Reducing Triangles

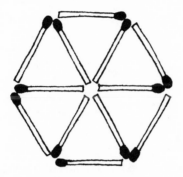

As in the previous puzzle, form six equilateral triangles with twelve matches. Can you rearrange two matches so as to eliminate one triangle? The triangles may now differ in size. Can you reduce the number of triangles to two by the same procedure? Do not double up two matches on one place.

12 / Reducing an Area

When the ratio of the three sides of a triangle is 3 : 4 : 5, it is a right triangle. This one is made with twelve matches. Let's say that the area of a square surrounded by four matches is one unit. The area of this right triangle is therefore six square units. (Remember that the area of a triangle is found by multiplying one-half the base by the height.) Here are three tasks:

1. Change the positions of two matches and make the area five units.
2. Move two more matches and reduce the area to four units.
3. Move two more matches to make the area three units.

13 / Two and One

This is a continuation of the previous puzzle. So far we have reduced the area of the figure to three square units, but we cannot reduce it further by the same procedure.

Now try to obtain an area of two units by rearranging the matches to form a completely different figure. Finally, reduce the area to one unit.

14 / Halving an Area

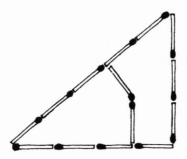

Form a right triangle with twelve matches. As before, the area of a square enclosed by four matches is called one unit. The area of this triangle is therefore six square units.

If we place two matches as shown in the illustration, they divide the triangle exactly into halves; that is, into two areas of three units each.

Here are the problems:

1. Using three matches instead of two, divide the area into two halves, each with three units.
2. Get the same result with four matches.

15 / Matching Names to Hair

Three foreigners were teasing a tour guide. All spoke Japanese fluently. The man with black hair said, "Our names are White, Black, and Brown."

Mr. White then said, "As you see, the colors of our hair are also white, black, and brown. But the colors and the names do not match for any of us."

From the conversation, can you match each man's name with the right hair color?

16 / Who Will Marry Whom?

"I have been asked to serve as the best man for three wedding ceremonies. I'm terribly busy."

"Oh, my! You must be."

An inquisitive fellow heard about the weddings. He visited the prospective brides and bridegrooms to find out who was to marry whom. His findings were a bit confusing, however:

1. Mr. A said that he was going to marry Miss X.
2. Miss X told the man that her future husband was Mr. C.
3. Mr. C said he was going to marry Miss Z.

The truth is, all three told lies.

The three men are A, B, and C. The three women are X, Y, and Z. Can you determine who will marry whom?

17 / Who Saw the Movie?

Only one of five friends saw a movie last week. I asked all five and they responded as below. Of the three statements each made, only two are correct; one is wrong. Find out who saw the movie.

A said: 1. I did not see the movie.
2. I have not seen any movie this past month.
3. D saw the movie.

B said: 4. I did not see the movie.
5. I passed by the movie theater.
6. I read a review of the movie.

C said: 7. I did not see the movie.
8. I read a review of the movie.
9. D saw the movie.

D said: 10. I did not see the movie.
11. E saw the movie.
12. A said I saw it, but that is not true.

E said: 13. I did not see the movie.
14. B saw the movie.
15. I read a review of the movie.

18 / What Color Is the Hat?

There are three red hats and two white hats. Three people—A, B, and C—are wearing hats, and the two unused ones have been concealed. A, B, and C do not know the color of their own hats, but each can see the color of the hat worn by the other two.

A was asked the following question: "Do you know the color of your hat?" He answered, "No, I don't know."

When the same question was asked of B, he said, "I don't know either."

The fact is that both A and B had red hats.

Lastly, C was asked the same question. He had been listening to the questions and answers of A and B, and answered with confidence, "Yes, the color of my hat is ———."

What color did he name?

19 / Who Is the Honest Member?

At a coffee shop, three friends told me about the Liars Club, whose members always tell lies. "Are you all members of the Liars Club?" I asked. A said something in response, but a passing train made it impossible for me to hear what he said.

Then B said to me, "A says he is not a member. A is indeed not a member and neither am I." Having heard that, C interjected, "B *is* a member, though I am not."

From this conversation, determine the one person who is the member. Assume that the two who are not members never tell lies.

20 / The Broken Window

Several children were playing in my backyard. Suddenly I heard the noise of a window breaking. I dashed out and saw four children looking at pieces of broken glass in my garage. Surely one of the children must have broken the garage window.

"John broke the window," said Ann.

"No, Gail did it," said John, grinning.

Gail's sister Sally declared, "It wasn't me!"

Gail said, "Me? John is a liar to say I did it."

Of the four children only one spoke the truth. Who is the culprit?

21 / Two Coin-Jumping Puzzles

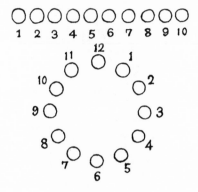

Here are two versions of a classic coin puzzle.

A. Put ten coins in a single row from left to right (top figure). Pick up any coin, jump over two adjacent coins, and place it on the third one. Repeat this five times to form five stacks of two coins each. You may jump either single coins or stacks of two coins.

B. Arrange twelve coins like the face of a clock (bottom figure). Pick up any coin, jump over the next two, and put it on the third coin. You may move in either direction. Repeat this six times to form six stacks of two coins each.

22 / How Many Turns?

Two coins touch each other. B is stationary, and A revolves around B. After A has made one circuit around B, how many times has it rotated 360 degrees?

23 / Coin Pyramids

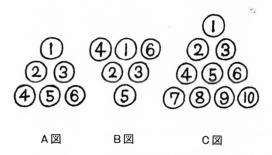

A図　　　　B図　　　　　C図

Place six coins as shown in Figure A so that their outline forms a pyramid. If you want to change this to an inverted pyramid by moving the smallest number of coins to different positions, move 4 and 6 to the top, as in Figure B. In this way you can invert the pyramid by moving only two coins.

How about the pyramid in Figure C? What is the smallest number of coins you must move to turn the pyramid upside down?

24 / Five Coins

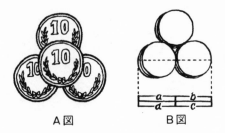

A 図   B 図

We have five coins. If we place four as in Figure A, all are in direct contact with one another. Let's try to do the same thing with five coins. Each coin must be touching the other four.

You might suppose you could solve this puzzle in the manner shown in Figure B. However, this is not a legitimate solution. Below the coins in Figure B is shown a side view. If coins A and C touch each other, B and D cannot. If B and D touch each other, A and C cannot.

Nevertheless, there is a legitimate solution with five coins.

25 / Four Pennies

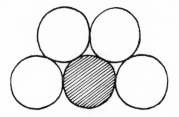

We wish to arrange four pennies on a table as shown, so that if a fifth penny goes into the shaded region it will touch the other four. We are not, however, allowed to use a fifth coin to make the arrangement accurate.

Using nothing more than the four coins, and by sliding them to different positions, how can you arrange them precisely in the desired formation?

26 / Six Pennies

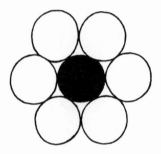

We wish to arrange six pennies in a ring, as shown by the white circles, so that if a seventh penny were placed on the black spot in the center it would fit perfectly.

As in the previous puzzle, we must achieve the arrangement without using a seventh penny as a guide. We must do it only by sliding the six pennies about on the table. We are not allowed to pick up a coin and put it down in another spot, and of course we must not mark the tabletop in any way or use a ruler to measure distances.

27 / Five Coins

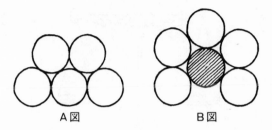

A図   B図

Arrange five coins on the table as shown in Figure A. We wish to rearrange them as in Figure B, so that when we put a sixth coin in the center it will touch the other five.

The rules for the two previous puzzles also apply here.

28 / Counterfeit Coin

A coin collector had nine coins. Eight were made of pure gold and all weighed exactly the same. A ninth coin, a counterfeit, was slightly lighter than the others. All nine were the same size, and by holding them in your hand you could not tell the difference between them.

We have a pair of balance scales, but there are no balance weights. All you can do is to put coins on each of the pans and see which side is heavier. Can you find the counterfeit in just two weighings?

29 / Pachinko Balls

There are six small pachinko balls (like pinballs). Five are the same weight and one is different. All six balls look alike, and it is not known whether the odd ball is lighter or heavier than the others.

Using a spring scale, identify the odd ball in just three separate weighings. At the same time, tell how many grams a standard ball weighs and how many grams the odd ball weighs.

30 / Counterfeit Coins

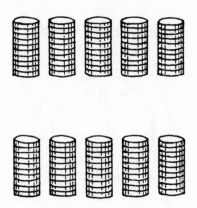

As the illustration shows, there are ten piles of money, each consisting of ten silver coins. All the coins in one pile are counterfeit, but we do not know which pile that is. We know the correct weight of a legal coin, and we know that the counterfeit coin weighs one gram more than a genuine one.

Using a spring scale, identify the pile of counterfeit coins by only one weighing.

31 / Three Cards

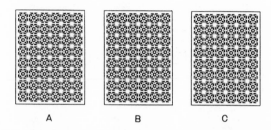

A   B   C

Three playing cards are face down on the table. With the help of the following clues, find the value of each card:

1. The total value of A and B is 15.
2. The total value of B and C is 17.
3. No card is a 7 or has a value higher than 9.

32 / Three Cards

Three cards lie face down in a row.

1. There is a queen on the right of a king.
2. There is a queen on the left of a queen.
3. There is a spade on the left of a heart.
4. There is a spade on the right of a spade.

Identify the three cards.

33 / Atezan I

Atezan is a mathematical game in which you can guess a number that a friend has in mind. Ask your friend to think of any number. Then tell him to perform in his head a series of five arithmetic calculations and tell you the final result. From this result you can guess his original number. How do you do it?

The five arithmetic calculations are:

1. Multiply the chosen number by 5.
2. Add 6 to the product.
3. Multiply the sum by 4.
4. Add 9 to the product.
5. Multiply the sum by 5.

34 / Atezan II

This is a version of the previous game in which you tell your friend his final result without asking a single question. For example, he thinks of a number, then after some mental calculations you say, "The result is five, isn't it?" And you are right.

Let's assume his chosen number is 597. The calculations you tell him to make are as follows:

1. Add the number that is larger by 1 than the number chosen (597 + 598 = 1195).
2. Add 9 to the sum (1195 + 9 = 1204).
3. Divide the sum by 2 (1204 ÷ 2 = 602).
4. Subtract the original number from the quotient (602 − 597 = 5).

Can you prove that the final result is always 5?

35 / Subtract 105

"How old are you?"

"What do you think?"

"May I take a guess?"

"Sure."

"All right. Please divide your age by three. What is the remainder?"

"It's two."

"If you divide your age by five, what is the remainder?"

"None."

"How about dividing your age by seven?"

"The remainder is one."

"I see . . . you are fifty years old, aren't you?"

"Amazing! You are right!"

By knowing the remainders when a person divides his age by three, five, and seven, you can determine his age. How is it done?

36 / Watch Puzzle

In this trick you guess the number on a clock or watch that someone selects in his mind.

Suppose you ask a friend to think of an hour number on a watch face. You say, "I shall point to various numbers on the face of your watch with a pencil. At each number you must count silently, beginning with the number that is next higher than the number you are thinking of. For example, if you are thinking of five, start counting six, seven, eight, and so on. When you count twenty, say, 'Stop.' My pencil will then be pointing to the number you first selected."

The trick never fails to work. How do you do it?

37 / Incorrect Watches

Four people (A, B, L, M) were relaxing. I approached them and asked, "What time is it?"

Mr. A looked at his wristwatch and answered, "It is six minutes to one."

Mr. B consulted his watch and said, "No, it is three minutes to one."

"Oh, dear, I have three minutes past one," said Miss L.

"My watch says two minutes after one," said Miss M.

The truth of the matter was that they were wrong by two minutes, three minutes, four minutes, and five minutes. (This order does not, however, correspond to the order of their replies.) Can you calculate the correct time and state by how many minutes each person was wrong?

38 / An Average-Speed Paradox

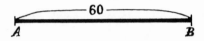

The distance between A and B is 60 kilometers. We went by car at a speed of 20 km per hour and the trip took 3 hours. On our way back we drove 30 km per hour and it took 2 hours. The round trip took 5 hours. If at all times we had driven at a steady 25 km.p.h. (the average of 20 km and 30 km), we would have made the round trip of 120 km in 4 hours and 48 minutes (120/25 = 4 and 4/5). This is 12 minutes less than 5 hours.

Now consider the problem from another angle. If we drive 5 hours at a constant speed of 25 km per hour, we can go 125 km. There is a difference of 5 km. Can you explain this paradox?

39 / Mystery of the Percentage

A company employs one hundred workers, of which sixty are men and forty women. During one month three men were absent, so the male absentee rate for the month was 5 percent. Four women were absent, so the female absentee rate was 10 percent.

The overall absentee rate was 7 percent, because seven out of one hundred persons were absent. However, let's consider men and women separately and calculate the overall average:

$$\frac{.05 + .10}{2} = 0.075$$

The result is 7.5 percent. Explain the discrepancy.

40 / A Family Survey

With father	Without father	Total
88 percent	12 percent	100 percent

With mother	Without mother	Total
95 percent	5 percent	100 percent

As part of a family survey, a school checked to see how many students did not have a father or a mother. The results are shown above.

Subtract the 5 percent who do not have a mother from the 88 percent who have a father and you get a balance of 83 percent. Now subtract the 12 percent without a father from the 95 percent with a mother, and you again get 83 percent. Is this always the case, regardless of the data, or is it a remarkable coincidence?

41 / Boys and Girls

A class of 50 students consists of 26 boys and 24 girls. We divide the students into two groups—30 in Group A, 20 in Group B.

The exact numbers of boys and girls in each group are unknown. We do know that the proportion of boys in Group A is larger than that of girls in Group B. How many more boys are there in Group A than girls in Group B?

42 / Fill in the Numbers

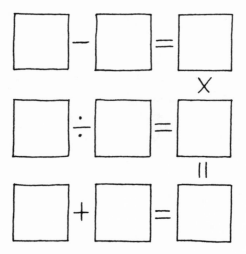

Write a different digit in each of the nine squares so that the three horizontal expressions and the single vertical one are all correct. You must use each digit from 1 through 9, and you may not use the same digit twice.

The interesting aspect of this puzzle is that all nine positive digits and all four arithmetical operations are used.

43 / Rubber Disk

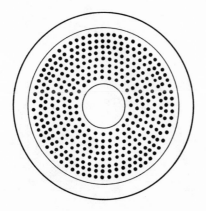

Pictured is a rubber disk often found on the counter of a store near the cash register. It is covered with hundreds of little rubber spikes, which keep coins from slipping and make it easy for the cashier to pick them up.

There are eight circles of spikes. The inner circle has twenty-four, the outer circle, sixty-six. The numbers are in arithmetical progression, which means that each circle has k more spikes than the next smaller one. Without counting all the dots in the picture, can you calculate the total number of spikes?

44 / Identical Areas

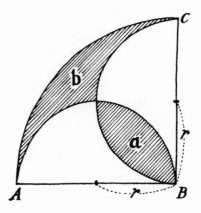

Inside this quarter-circle are two semicircles with the same radius, r. Can you prove that the shaded lens shape (a) is equal in area to the shaded portion (b) that looks like a ginkgo leaf?

45 / Walking on the Tatami

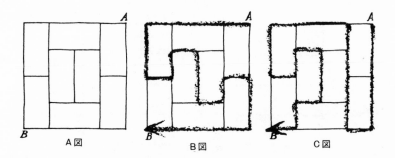

A 図   B 図   C 図

The floor of a room is covered with *tatami* (mats). Let's walk along the edges of each mat, starting at the top right corner A and going to the lower left corner B. We wish to take the longest course without going along any border twice. What path should we follow?

Figure C shows a longer path than does Figure B. But there is a path longer than either of these. Can you find it?

46 / How to Lay the Tatami

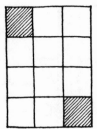 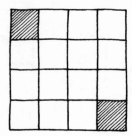

The figure on the left is the floor plan of a room. The two shaded squares are staircases. It is easy to put five *tatami* (mats), each covering two squares, in this room. Is it possible to put seven *tatami* on the floor of the room shown in the illustration on the right? You are not permitted to overlap mats or to cut them.

47 / Cutting a Greek Cross

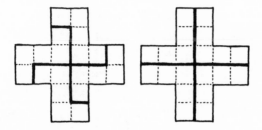

We wish to cut a Greek cross into four pieces of the same size and shape. The illustration shows two ways to do it. Can you find other solutions?

48 / Halving a Square

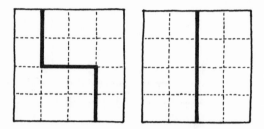

A square piece of paper is divided into sixteen smaller squares. There are six ways of cutting it into two pieces of the same size and shape.

Two solutions are shown above. Please find the other four. You may cut only along the dotted lines, and you may not match the shapes by turning over one of the cut pieces. You may, however, rotate any piece to make it fit the other.

49 / Cutting a Square into Four Equal Pieces

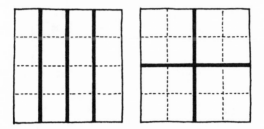

This is a variation on the previous puzzle. We want to cut the same square into four pieces of equal size and shape. The rules of the previous problem also apply to this one.

You see two solutions; there are four others. Can you find them?

50 / The Big Dipper

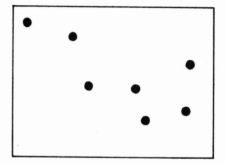

Here you see the seven stars of the Big Dipper. Draw three straight lines that will put each star in a separate region of the rectangle.

51 / How Many Ways?

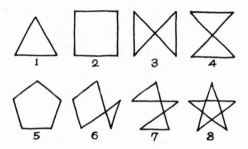

Put three dots on a piece of paper to mark the three corners of a triangle. Figure 1 shows the only way to connect those three points by straight lines forming a continuous path that ends on the point from which it started.

There are two different ways to join the points of a square. See Figures 2 and 3 (Figure 4 is simply a rotation of Figure 3). In the case of a regular pentagon, there are four different ways to connect the points with a continuous line, as you can see in Figures 5, 6, 7, and 8. Find all the ways to join the six corners of a regular hexagon. Remember: the path must visit each point and return to its starting place.

52 / Shimi (Paper Moths)

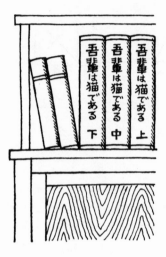

On the shelf stand volumes 1, 2, and 3 of the first edition of Soseki's *I Am a Cat*. The books have been lying there for a long time, and moths have dug a tunnel from page one of volume 1 to the last page of volume 3. The paper in each volume is 3 centimeters thick and its cover is 1 centimeter (front and back covers are 5 millimeters each). Can you tell how long the tunnel is?

53 / Ten Pairs of Socks

A girl had twenty socks in a drawer. There were ten red socks and ten green ones. One night, just as she was going to take out a pair of socks, the lights went out. If she wants to get a pair of the same color, red or green, what is the smallest number of socks she must take out of the drawer? Assume that the socks are all mixed up.

54 / A Raise in Salary

An American company is preparing two plans of yearly salary advancement for its employees:

Plan A: The initial salary is $100, to be raised $20 each year.

Plan B: The initial salary is also $100, to be increased $5 every half year.

In either case the salary is calculated every half year. If you worked for the company, which plan would you prefer?

55 / Dividing Cells

A biochemist is cultivating living cells. Each cell splits into two cells after one minute. One minute later the two cells split to make four, then the four become eight, and so on. Every minute the number of cells doubles.

Assume that it takes an hour for one cell to grow until a bottle is filled. If the chemist starts with two cells, how long will it take to fill the same bottle?

56 / Who Won?

Two brothers decided to run a 100-meter race. The older brother won by 3 meters. In other words, when the older brother reached the finish, the younger brother had run 97 meters.

They decided to race again, this time with the older brother starting 3 meters behind the starting line. Assuming that both boys ran the second race at the same speed as before, who do you think won?

57 / 100-Meter Dash

When A and B ran a 100-meter dash, A won by 10 meters. B then raced 100 meters against C, and B won by 10 meters.

If A and C raced, running the same distance of 100 meters, by how many meters would A win?

58 / A Curious Cube

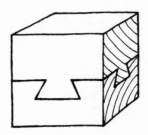

Look carefully at the illustration. Two pieces of wood are joined together to make a cube. The two hidden sides of the cube look exactly like the two sides that you see. It appears impossible to separate the two parts of the cube, yet their internal structure permits them to slide apart easily. How can this be?

59 / A Dog and Two Travelers

Two men were traveling with a dog. A's walking speed is 3 km per hour. B's walking speed is 6 km per hour.

One morning A left the hotel by himself and walked down a road for 3 km before B left the hotel with the dog. While B walked down the same road, the dog playfully trotted back and forth between the two men at a speed of 10 km per hour. How many kilometers had the dog run by the time B caught up with A?

60 / Which Line Is Longer?

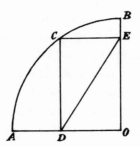

Lines AO and BO are of equal length. They meet at a right angle. A circular arc joins A and B. Draw a rectangle CDOE anywhere inside this area. C may be at any point on the arc.

Join D and E to make a diagonal in the rectangle. Is this diagonal DE longer, shorter, or the same length as AO? It is hard to believe, but it is not necessary to know the lengths of any of the line segments in the figure.

61 / The Missing Yen

Three men stayed at an inn. Their bill was 30,000 yen
and each guest put up 10,000 yen. The money, along with
the bill, was taken to the cashier by the maid.

In the meantime the inn, as a token of good will, had
reduced the amount of the bill by 5,000 yen. From the
balance of 5,000 yen the maid took 2,000 and returned only
3,000 to the men. They split this three ways, so each man
received a refund of 1,000 yen. Since each paid 10,000
yen and received 1,000 yen, he spent 9,000 yen.

Each man paid 9,000 yen, so that the total spent by all
three was 27,000 yen. The maid took 2,000 yen. These
two amounts add up to 29,000 yen. What happened to the
remaining 1,000 yen?

62 / Guessing Ages

Three sales clerks were introduced to a new employee. After she had left, the first employee said, "How old is she? I imagine she is twenty-one."

"Twenty-three, I think," the second employee answered.

The third man said, "I think she's older. My guess is twenty-five."

The three clerks were all wrong. Two were one year off; the other missed by three years. How old is the new employee?

63 / A Paper-Folding Puzzle

Fold a piece of paper in two, allowing a margin of one centimeter, as shown in Figure 1. Crease the paper sharply at the bottom. Then draw the shorter side up one centimeter, to make it even with the other edge, as in Figure 2, but do not crease the paper. Draw the same side up one more centimeter so that it resembles Figure 3. Crease the paper at the bottom. How many centimeters are there between the two creases?

64 / Eight Squares

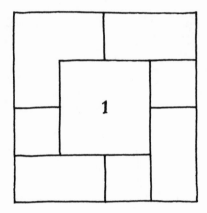

Eight square sheets of paper, all the same size, have been placed on a table. They overlap as shown in the illustration. One sheet (1) is shown completely, and the seven others are only partly exposed. Number the squares in order from the top layer to the bottom.

65 / Eight More Squares

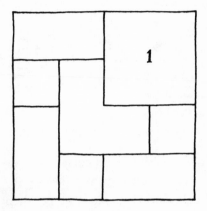

This is a variation on the previous puzzle. Number the square pieces of paper from the top layer to the bottom.

66 / Adding a Square

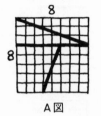

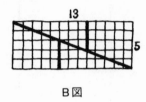

A図   B図

This is a well known but poorly understood paradox. Many readers may have been puzzled by it.

Cut the checkerboard (a piece of graph paper will do nicely) into four pieces as shown by the bold lines in Figure A. Then rearrange the pieces as in Figure B. Strangely enough, Figure A has sixty-four small squares, but B has sixty-five. Where did the extra square come from?

67 / Disappearing Squares

Is it possible to rearrange the four pieces of Puzzle 66 in a different way so as to decrease the number of small squares to sixty-three? If so, how?

68 / Crossing the River

Three adults and three children went for a walk and found themselves at a riverbank.

There was no bridge to cross the river, but they discovered a boat moored at the shore. It was so small that it could carry only one adult or two children at a time.

How could all six of them cross the river to the other side, and what would be the smallest number of trips necessary?

69 / Jealous Couples

Three wives were traveling with their husbands. They came to a riverbank, where they found only a small boat capable of carrying two persons at a time. The men promptly decided that no woman could ride in the boat or remain on the riverbank with any man except her own husband.

How did the three couples cross the river, and what was the smallest number of moves?

70 / How to Measure Four Liters

A man went to a river to get 4 liters of water. He had only two containers, one 5-liter can and one 3-liter can. Neither of the cans was marked for smaller measures.

How did the man obtain exactly 4 liters?

71 / Measuring Oil I

This famous puzzle is from Mitsuyoshi Yoshida's book *Junkooki* (1631). It was the first puzzle of this type to appear in print in Japan.

The task is to divide 10 *sho* of oil into two equal parts. The oil is in a 10-*sho* container. We also have one 7-*sho* container and one 3-*sho* container. Both containers are empty.

72 / Measuring Oil II

This complicated puzzle was given to me by Mr. Thomas O'Beirne.

A 22-liter wine barrel is filled with wine. There are also a 12-liter container and a 7-liter container, both empty. The containers have no measurement marks, and there are no other containers to be used. We want 1 liter of wine in each of the two containers. The unwanted 20 liters may be discarded as the operations proceed. It can be done in thirty-five operations. I shall not give the answer, so that you may have the pleasure of solving it for yourself.

73 / Down by the Riverside

This is a famous pouring problem devised by H. E. Dudeney. A man went to a stream with a 15-pint container and a 16-pint container, both empty. What should he do to get 8 pints of water?

As before, filling the container with water, emptying it, or transferring the water from one container to the other will each be considered as one operation. The task is to obtain 8 pints in the smallest number of operations.

74 / The Disappearing Penny

This classic brain teaser still confounds people. In England, one hundred years ago, two women were selling apples on the street. One sells 3 apples for a penny; the other, 2 apples for a penny.

One day both women had to leave the street for a time. Each had 30 apples left, and they asked a friend to sell the 60 apples at 5 for 2 pennies. If the two women had sold the apples separately, they would have obtained 25 pennies between them: 10 pennies for one lady, 15 pennies for the other.

Because they put their remaining apples together, however, they made only 24 pennies. When the ladies returned, they thought at first that their friend had stolen a penny, which of course he hadn't. But where did the missing penny go?

75 / Angle on a Cube

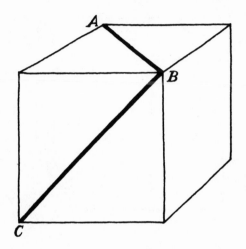

AB and BC are diagonals on two faces of a cube. What degree is the angle ABC?

76 / Cutting Cheese

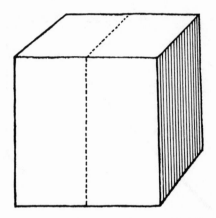

We want to cut this cube of cheese into two identical parts, each with a cross-section shaped like a regular hexagon. If the cut is vertical, as shown by the dotted lines, the cross-sections (new surfaces) will be squares. How can we angle the cutting plane to produce regular hexagons?

77 / Tracing Televisions

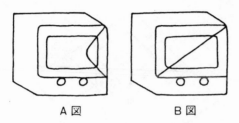

A 図   B 図

The illustration shows two television sets. To draw Figure A in one continuous line, without taking the pencil off the paper, you may start and finish at any point. Try it and you will see how easy it is.

For Figure B there are only two points from which to draw the picture in one stroke. Can you find them?

78 / Rolling Dice

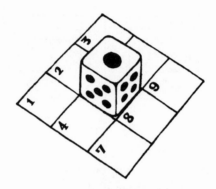

Draw a three-by-three matrix of squares each the same size as the face of a die. Place the die, with the ace on top, on the center square as shown in the illustration.

You may roll the die in four directions: up, down, left, or right, but never diagonally. By rolling we mean to tip the die so that it makes a quarter-turn to an adjacent square. Each time you roll the die, its upper face changes. The task is to roll the die until it is on square 7 with its 6-face uppermost and to do this in the fewest possible rolls.

79 / Geometry of the Billiard Table

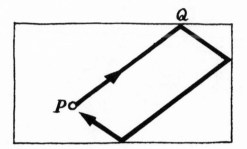

There is a game called three-cushion billiards, in which you must hit the cushion three times with the cue ball before you hit the two object balls.

Suppose you put a ball at P on the billiard table and hit it in the direction shown by the arrow. Your aim is to make the ball hit the upper side of the table at Q, then the right side, and then the bottom side, so the ball will finally cross P. You are not permitted to use "English" on the ball.

How can you determine the location of Q?

80 / Moving Nine Chips

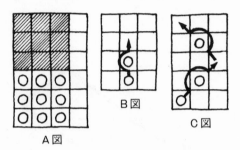

A ⊠   B ⊠

                                                    C ⊠

The board for this puzzle consists of a six-by-four array of squares. Put a chip or pebble on each of nine squares as shown in Figure A. Your aim is to move all nine chips up to the nine shaded squares while observing the following rules:

1. You may move a chip to any empty square in any direction: up, down, left, right, or diagonally.

2. You may jump over another chip in any direction to an empty square (see Figure B).

3. You may continue jumping as many times as you like, if the pattern permits (see Figure C). A chain of jumps counts as one move.

What is the smallest number of moves needed to transfer all nine chips to the shaded squares?

81 / Elevator Puzzle

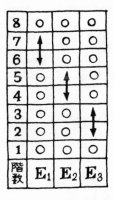

The picture represents an eight-story building. It has three elevators, each of which stops at only the floors marked with circles in the illustration. You can thereby get from one floor to any other by riding just one elevator.

Now suppose that each elevator stops at only *three* floors between floors one and eight. What would be the smallest number of elevators that would allow a visitor to go from one floor to any other by riding only one elevator?

82 / A Path Puzzle

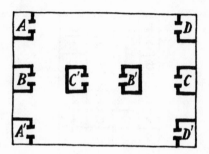

The illustration shows eight houses and their front doors. The problem is to draw a line from the door of A to the door of A', another line that joins the doors of B and B', a third line that joins C to C', and a fourth that joins D to D'. No line may cross another line, pass through the sides of a house, or cross the outside rectangular border of the picture. The problem may seem impossible to solve, but it can be done.

83 / Footprints in the Snow

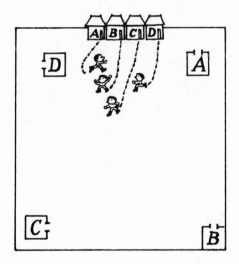

Each of four children lives in one of the houses A, B, C, and D. Each goes to a different school. One morning after a snowstorm there were footprints of the four students in the snow. The footprints showed that no child crossed the path of another child on the way to school.

Can you draw four paths showing how each child walked from his house to the school that bears the same letter as his house? No path may cross another or go outside the picture's border.

84 / Planning a Trip

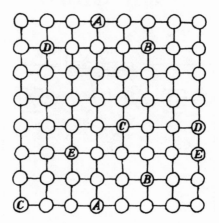

This is a stylized map on which circles represent towns and lines represent roads. One car drives from A to A, another car from B to B, a third from C to C, a fourth from D to D, and a fifth from E to E. Show how this can be done so that no path crosses another.

85 / Dividing a Triangle

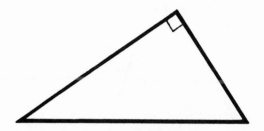

We wish to divide this right triangle into smaller acute triangles, each of whose angles is less than 90 degrees. Can it be done? If so, what is the smallest number of acute triangles into which it can be divided?

86 / Overlapping Triangles

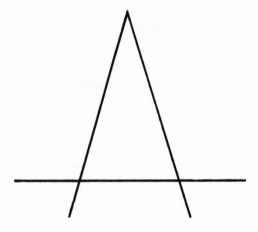

These three lines form only one triangle. Draw two more straight lines to create ten triangles. The triangles may overlap one another.

87 / Letter W

Can you add three straight lines to this letter W to get nine triangles? In this problem we count only triangles that do not overlap in any way.

88 / Fujimura's Triangle Puzzle

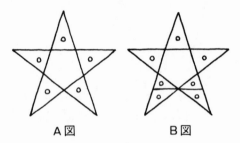

A図   B図

Figure A shows how to make as many nonoverlapping triangles as possible with five straight lines. The maximum is five triangles.

With six straight lines you can create seven triangles, as shown in Figure B. How many nonoverlapping triangles can you make with seven straight lines?

89 / Closing the Links

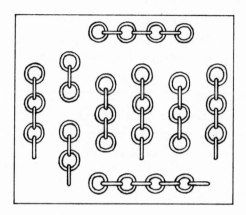

We wish to join these 9 pieces of chain to make a closed ring of 50 links. It costs 10 yen to open one ring and 20 yen to close it again. We can buy a new ring of 50 links for 250 yen. Can we make a ring from the 9 pieces for less?

90 / A Clock Puzzle

Between noon today and noon tomorrow, how many times does the long hand of a clock pass the short hand? "Pass" means that one hand follows, overtakes, and goes ahead of the other. Since both hands are at the same spot at noon, the long hand does not pass the short hand at twelve o'clock, the starting time.

To answer the question, you may look at your watch, but you may not move its hands.

91 / College Baseball

	A	B	C	D	E
A					
B				O	
C					
D		X			
E					

Five colleges, A, B, C, D, and E, played a round robin baseball tournament, each team playing once against every other team.

By drawing lots, B and D played the opening game. We have recorded B's win with a circle on the chart shown above. After that, the tournament results were as follows:

Team	No. of Wins	No. of Losses
D	1	3
C	2	2
A	0	4
E	4	0

How should these results be recorded on the chart? How many games were played altogether?

92 / Six Experts

Six experts in their respective fields are on a train trip together. They sit facing each other in groups of three. They are an essayist, an archaeologist, a musician, a novelist, a playwright, and a poet. Each has written books in his special field and each is now reading a book by one of the others.

From the ten facts given below, state each man's profession.

1. A is reading essays.
2. C is reading a book written by the person sitting opposite him.
3. B is sitting between the essayist and the musician.
4. E is sitting next to the playwright.
5. The essayist is sitting opposite the archaeologist.
6. D is reading a book written by the playwright.
7. A is sitting in a corner and has no interest in archaeology.
8. D is sitting opposite the novelist.
9. E is reading a book written by the musician.
10. F has never read a book of poetry. Obviously, he is not a poet.

This is a typical logic problem by Hubert Phillips ("Caliban"), although I have reduced his list of facts from eleven to ten.

93 / Examination Results

Six students, A, B, C, D, E, and F, took a college entrance examination.

1. A and B received the same marks.
2. A was higher than C.
3. C was higher than D.
4. E was lower than A but higher than D.
5. E was lower than C.
6. B was lower than F.

Your task is to rank the six students in order from high to low.

94 / Going Shopping

Four people, A, B, C, and D, went to a department store together. One bought a watch, one a book, one a pair of shoes, and one a camera. The first, second, third, and fourth floors carry those items, but not necessarily in the order given for the purchases.

On the basis of the following clues, determine who bought what on which floor:

1. A went to the first floor.
2. Watches are sold on the fourth floor.
3. C went to the second floor.
4. B bought a book.
5. A did not buy a camera.

95 / Children of Three Families

I am 13 years old. Some time ago 12 children (including me) gathered at my home—4 children each from 3 families, A, B, and C, including mine. Interestingly enough, each child was of a different age and together represented 12 of the numbers from 1 to 13. In other words, one of the ages was not represented by a child.

For the fun of it, I added up the ages of the children in each family and got the following results:

Family A: Total of 41 years, including the 12 year old.

Family B: Total of 22 years, including the 5 year old.

Family C: Total of 21 years, including the 4 year old.

Only Family A had two children who were born one year apart.

Can you answer two questions?

1. To which family do I belong—A, B, or C?

2. How old are the children in each family?

96 / Cutting Cards

Can you cut a three-by-five file card or a postcard to make a large ring that you can pass over your entire body? Use only scissors. You may not use glue or paste or any kind of sticky tape.

97 / A Switching Task

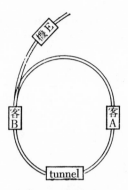

A portion of railway track has the shape shown in the illustration. You see two passenger cars A and B, an engine E, and a tunnel at the bottom, between the two cars. The single switch can be changed at any time.

The lengths of the tunnel and the two cars are the same. The engine is too tall to go through the tunnel. It can be used only to push the cars into the tunnel and pull them out on the other side. The cars can be joined for pulling.

The task is to exchange the positions of the passenger cars, A and B, then return the engine to its original position.

98 / Four Explorers

Four men, A, B, C, and D, went on an exploration trip. Each carried enough food to last 5 days. If all four traveled together, they could advance for 2½ days and then return to the base in another 2½ days.

The explorers put their heads together and devised a way to cover more territory. Each day, one of the men gave some of his food to the others and returned to the base, keeping the food he needed for the trip back. Through this procedure one man could go farther than the others and still return home. How many days did he travel?

SOLUTIONS

1

Slide the horizontal match half its length to the right. Move the match on the left to the lower right.

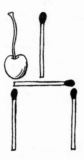

Martin Gardner contributed this puzzle to *Scientific American* in 1967 and it immediately became popular in Japan, where for some reason it was called *Garbage and Dustpan* instead of *Cherry and Glass*.

2

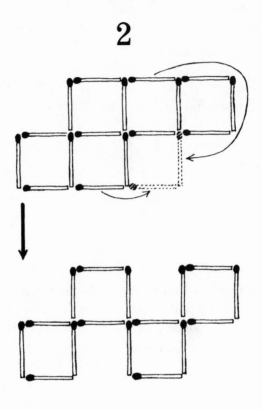

3

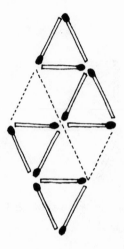

Remove the four matches indicated by dotted lines and you get the right answer.

4

This charming puzzle was created, I believe, during the Taisho era (1912–1926).

5

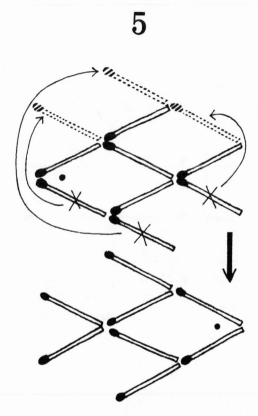

The idea of changing the fish's direction may have been adapted from the preceding match dog puzzle. I believe that this puzzle was invented in the Showa era (1926– present).

6

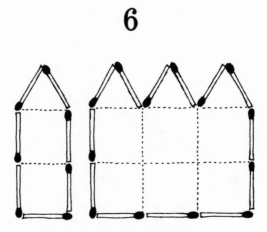

The dotted lines show that one area has two squares and one equilateral triangle and that the other area has six squares and three equilateral triangles. Note that twelve horizontal and vertical matches have not been touched.

7

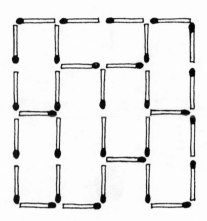

The illustration shows how to do it. Nine is the smallest number of matches that can be removed to obtain this result.

8

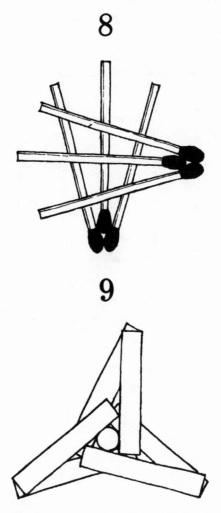

9

Gardner's book carries the illustration shown above. Isn't the solution magnificent?

The circle in the center is an end view of the seventh match, placed so as to touch the other six.

10

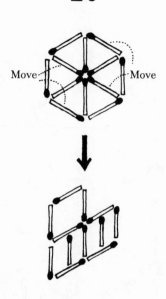

This illustration is only one of many answers. Check to
see that there are twelve parallelograms in all.

11

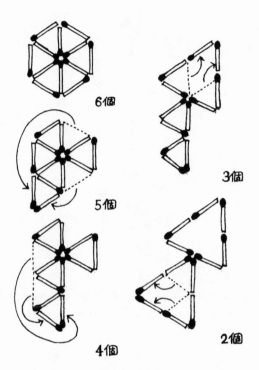

If you look at the figures from top to bottom you will see the solution. Of course there are others. This one is by Michio Matsuda.

12

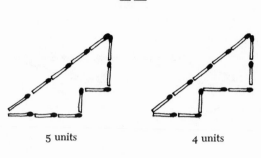

5 units   4 units

3 units

13

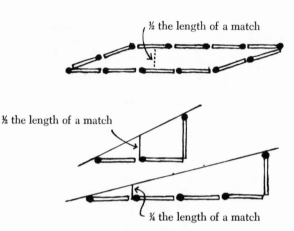

Form a parallelogram as shown above, with a height half the length of a match. To obtain an area of just one unit, make the height one-fourth the length of a match. The illustrations show how to find these two measurements.

14

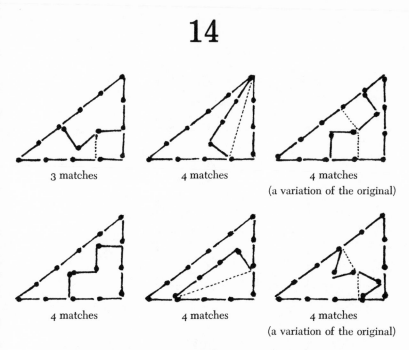

3 matches   4 matches   4 matches
                                                (a variation of the original)

4 matches   4 matches   4 matches
                                                (a variation of the original)

The dotted lines bisect the triangles. With four matches there are five different answers. (You can use up to ten matches to bisect the area of a right triangle.)

Mr. Naomitsu Shibata introduced this puzzle in *Sankei Puzzles,* but the original source is unknown.

15

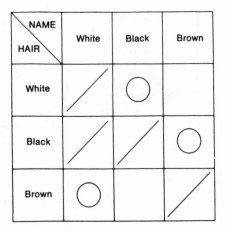

NAME / HAIR	White	Black	Brown
White	╱	◯	
Black	╱	╱	◯
Brown	◯		╱

16

Let's analyze the words of Mr. A, Miss X, and Mr. C.

Mr. A's statement is a lie, so we know that he will *not* marry Miss X. But Miss X's statement is also untrue. Therefore, Miss X will marry neither Mr. A nor Mr. C, but Mr. B.

Mr. C's false statement, combined with the previous one, reveals that Mr. C will not marry Miss X or Miss Z. We conclude that Mr. C will marry Miss Y.

Finally, we see that Mr. A will marry Miss Z.

17

B saw it. We can prove this by examining all the answers.

Assume that A (1) is a lie and that A saw the movie. It follows that A (3) is also incorrect because only one person saw the movie. But since each person told only one lie, A (1) must be true. A did not see the movie.

By the same reasoning we applied to A's statements, we know that C, D, and E did not see the movie. Therefore, only B saw the movie.

Let's double-check to see whether our reasoning produces any contradictions:

The lies are A (3), B (4), C (9), D (11), and E (15). All the other statements are true. Therefore, there are no contradictions. Consequently, the person who saw the movie is B.

18

C named the color red. He knew his hat was red by the following reasoning: "Suppose my hat is white. A sees it is white. If A also sees a white hat on B, he will know his own hat is red and answer yes. But he answered no, which tells B that his hat is red. Therefore B will answer yes. However, B did *not* answer yes. Therefore, my original supposition must be false. My hat must be red."

19

If A is a member, he lies and will therefore say, "I am not a member." If A is not a member, he will also say, "I am not a member." In either case, he must say, "I am not a member."

B therefore spoke truly when he reported what A had said. This proves that B is not a member.

Thus, C's statement clearly is a lie, so we know that he is the honest member of the Liars Club.

20

If John broke the window, then Ann and Sally spoke the truth.

If Gail broke the window, John and Sally spoke the truth.

If Ann broke the window, Sally and Gail spoke the truth.

If Sally broke the window, Gail spoke the truth.

Only one child told the truth, so it is Sally who broke the window.

This puzzle was devised by J. A. H. Hunter, a Canadian puzzle inventor.

21

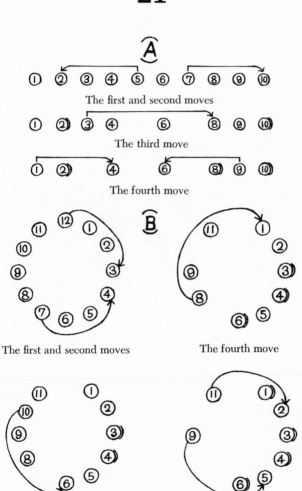

The first and second moves

The third move

The fourth move

The first and second moves   The fourth move

The third move   The fifth and sixth moves

Moves for solving each puzzle are shown in the illustration.

22

Since the circumferences of A and B are equal, you may
think the moving coin makes only one rotation. Try it and
you will find that it actually makes two complete rotations!

23

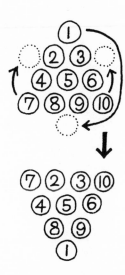

You can do it by moving only three coins. Move 1 to the bottom, 7 and 10 to the top.

24

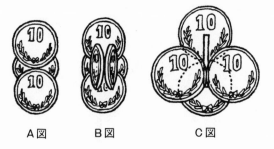

A 図   B 図   C 図

First, place three coins as shown in Figure A. Next, make the two remaining coins stand and touch at the top while the bottoms of the same coins meet the other three lying flat, as shown in Figure B.

A reader sent in another solution, which is shown in Figure C.

25

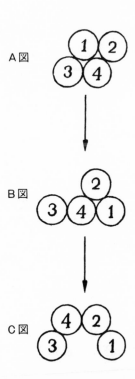

First place the four coins next to each other, as shown in Figure A. Move (1) to the new position shown in B.

Pull out (4) carefully and put it between (2) and (3), as shown in Figure C. It is now possible to place a fifth coin exactly in the spot where it touches all the other coins.

Look at Figure C. It is very difficult to measure the distance between (1) and (3) with your eyes, yet you have solved the problem beautifully by this method.

26

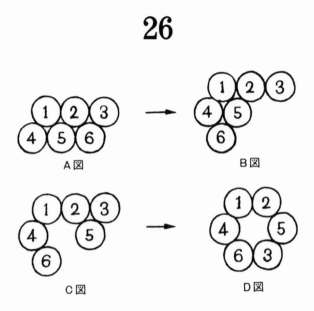

Start with the pennies as in Figure A. Move (6) carefully to the spot shown in B.

Next, slide (5) to touch (2) and (3), as in Figure C. Then move (3) to touch (6) and (5), as in D.

27

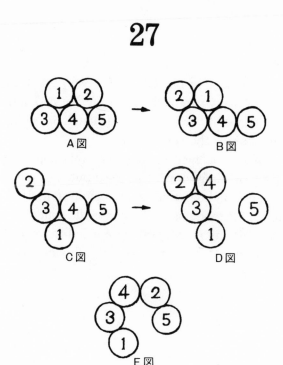

My solution is based on the preceding two puzzles, which use four and six coins. A puzzle with five coins was not known, so I filled the gap.

The relationships between the number of coins and the minimum number of moves are:

4 coins — 2 moves
5 coins — 4 moves
6 coins — 3 moves

28

Put any three coins on each of the two pans. If one side is lighter, take any two of the coins on that pan and weigh one against the other. If the two match in weight, the remaining coin is the counterfeit.

If the scales balance on the first weighing, you must check the remaining three coins. First put one coin on each pan. If one is lighter, that is the counterfeit. If the two sides match, the one not on the pan is the counterfeit.

This fascinating puzzle was introduced to Japan for the first time in the May 1947 issue of the Japanese edition of *Reader's Digest*.

29

Call the six balls A, B, C, D, E, and F. First, weigh A,
B, C, D together. Call the total weight W_1. Second, weigh
C, D, E together. Call the total weight W_2.

If $3W_1 = 4W_2$, we know that ball F is the odd ball. We
weigh it and our task is done.

If $3W_1$ does not equal $4W_2$, the third step is to weigh A
and C together. Call the total weight W_3. Listed below are
the five possible results, each indicating which ball is the
odd one and how much it weighs:

1. $W_1 = 2W_3$ . . . . Ball E (weight $= W_2 - W_3$)
2. $2W_2 = 3W_3$ . . . . Ball B (weight $= W_1 - W_2$)
3. $3 (W_1 - W_3) = 2W_2$ . . . Ball A (weight $= W_1 - W_2$)
4. $2 (W_1 - W_2) = W_3$ . . . . Ball D (weight $= W_2 - W_3$)
5. $W_1 - W_2 = W_2 - W_3$ . . Ball C (weight $= 2W_3 - W_2$)

Once we know which ball is different, it is easy to determine from our data the weight of a standard ball.

30

Select one coin from pile 1, two coins from pile 2, three coins from pile 3, and so forth. Place this set of fifty-five coins on the spring scales. Since you know how much fifty-five authentic coins should weigh, the excess weight in grams will identify the pile from which one or more counterfeit coins were taken. For example, if the excess is three grams, it means pile 3 has counterfeit coins.

31

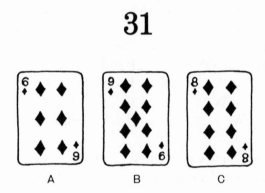

A   B   C

32

33

1. $n \times 5 = 5n$
2. $5n + 6$
3. $(5n + 6) \times 4 = 20n + 24$
4. $20n + 24 + 9 = 20n + 33$
5. $(20n + 33) \times 5 = 100n + 165$

In these equations n stands for the number your friend selected. Thus, if you subtract 165 from the final result of $100n + 165$, then divide the balance by 100, you will get n, the original number.

It is easy to invent other procedures that work as well as this one. By changing the numbers used in the calculations, you get different versions of the game.

34

1. $n + (n + 1) = 2n + 1$
2. $2n + 1 + 9 = 2n + 10$
3. $(2n + 10) \div 2 = n + 5$
4. $n + 5 - n = 5$

If you want to repeat this trick in front of the same people, you should change the formula so that the answer is different each time. The change occurs at step 2. Instead of adding 9, add any odd number, k. The final result will be $\dfrac{k + 1}{2}$. For example, if you add 11, the final product will be $\dfrac{11 + 1}{2} = 6$.

35

Multiply the first remainder by 70 ($2 \times 70 = 140$).
Multiply the second remainder by 21 ($0 \times 21 = 0$).
Multiply the third remainder by 15 ($1 \times 15 = 15$).
Add the three products ($140 + 0 + 15 = 155$).
Subtract 105 (or its multiple) from the sum ($155 - 105 = 50$).
If a, b, c are the remainders when a person's age is divided by 3, 5, and 7 respectively, the formula for calculating age is $\dfrac{70a + 21b + 15c}{105}$. The remainder is the age.

This formula is given in Japanese books on mathematics written in the Edo period (1598–1868).

This famous puzzle is called Hyakugo-Gen ("Subtract 105") because in the last step you subtract 105 as many times as possible. It appears in an old Chinese book on mathematics called *Sonshi Sankyo (Mathematical Bible of Military Science)*.

36

First, point to any seven numbers at random, pretending to be deep in thought. But the eighth time you point to a number, it must be 12. The ninth number must be 9, the tenth number 8, and so on as you go counterclockwise around the dial. When your friend reaches 20 and says, "Stop," you will be pointing to the number originally chosen.

37

A, who said it was six minutes to one, must be wrong by two, three, four, or five minutes. He cannot be wrong by two minutes, because that would make L (who said it was three minutes past one) wrong by seven minutes. Nor can he be wrong by three minutes, because that would make L wrong by six minutes. Therefore, A is wrong by four or five minutes.

Assume he is four minutes slow. The correct time would

be two minutes to one, and L would be five minutes fast. But this would make the other two persons wrong by one and four minutes, instead of the correct two and three minutes.

The only remaining possibility is that A is five minutes slow. The correct time would be one minute to one, and L would be four minutes fast. This would make B wrong by two minutes and M wrong by three minutes.

38

It is an error to think that the average speed for the round trip is 25 km. If each one-way trip had taken the same amount of time, the average speed would indeed have been 25 km. But if the amount of time is different each way, the average speed cannot be 25 km.

In this case, our round trip of 120 km was driven in 5 hours, so the correct average speed was $\frac{120}{5} = 24$ km.p.h. If we drove 5 hours at this speed, we would go 120 km, so there is no contradiction.

39

The first method of determining the overall rate of absenteeism is correct. We can see why the second method is faulty by considering an extreme case.

Suppose a company has 100 male workers and 1 female. During one month the woman does not work and 1 man does not work. The absentee rate for men is 1 percent and the absentee rate for women is 100 percent. Since only 2 persons were absent, out of a work force of 101, the overall absentee rate for the month is $\frac{2}{101,}$ or a trifle less than 2 percent.

Now let's figure it the incorrect way. We add the separate percentages for men and women to get 101 percent, then divide by 2 to get an average. The result is $\frac{1.01}{2} =$ a trifle more than 50 percent, which of course is absurd.

40

It is always the case, and we can prove this with elementary algebra.

Let x be the total number of students, a the number with a father, b the number without a father, c the number with a mother, d the number without a mother. The percentages are $a \div x$, $b \div x$, $c \div x$, and $d \div x$. The equality that seems so coincidental can now be expressed as:

$$\frac{A}{X} - \frac{D}{X} = \frac{C}{X} - \frac{B}{X}$$

The x's cancel out and we have $a - d = c - b$. These terms can be rearranged to make $a + b = c + d$. We know that $a + b$ equals $c + d$ because each side of the equality is the total number of students. Therefore, the result given in the problem is no coincidence but one that always obtains, regardless of the percentages in the data.

41

Let x = number of boys in Group A and y = number of girls in the same group.

$$x + y = 30, \text{ or } y = 30 - x$$

In Group B the number of girls = $24 - y$. So the difference between the boys in Group A and the girls in Group B is:

$$x - (24 - y)$$

Substituting for y the expression given in the first equation produces:
$$x - [24 - (30 - x)]$$

which gives the expression a value of 6. There are 6 more boys in Group A than there are girls in Group B.

42

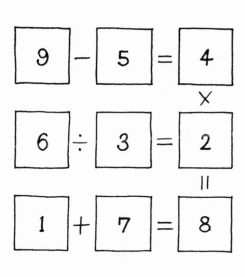

43

The formula for the sum of any arithmetical progression is:

$$\text{Sum} = \frac{n(a + b)}{2}$$

where n is the number of terms, a is the smallest term, and b is the largest. In this case:

$$\frac{8\,(24 + 66)}{2} = 360$$

Therefore, there are 360 spikes. This formula is so useful that it is worth memorizing.

44

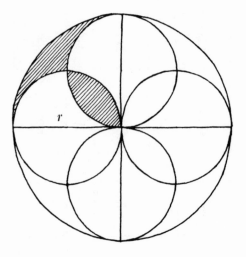

Here is the complete circle, enclosing four smaller ones. Its radius (r) is equal to each of their diameters, so that the area of the large circle (πr^2) is equal to the combined areas of the four smaller circles: $4\pi\left(\dfrac{r}{2}\right)^2 = 4\pi\left(\dfrac{r^2}{4}\right) = \dfrac{4\pi r^2}{4} = \pi r^2$.

The four ginkgo leaves represent the difference in area between the large circle and the four overlapping circles enclosed within it, just as the four lenses show the difference between the total area of the four small circles and the area they cover when they overlap. Since the large circle and the combined smaller ones have the same area, the lenses also represent the difference in area between the large circle and the overlapping smaller ones, and thus are equal to the area covered by the ginkgo leaves. The leaves are all of equal area, as are the lenses, so a lens and a leaf are equal.

45

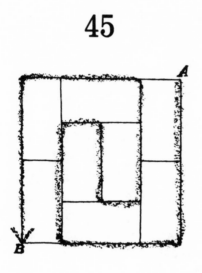

46

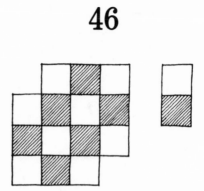

First color the floor squares alternately black and white like a checkerboard. There are eight white squares and six black ones. Since each *tatami* must cover one black square and one white square, we are bound to leave two white squares uncovered after laying down six *tatami*. Since the two squares cannot be adjacent, it will be impossible to cover them with the seventh mat.

This puzzle is found in Kentaro Yano's *Math After Dinner*.

47

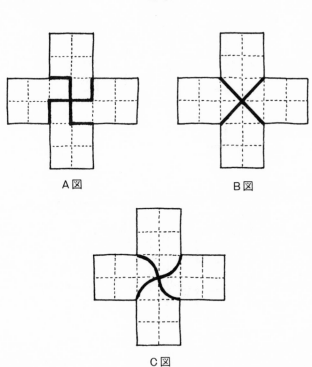

A 図   B 図

C 図

Figure A is the only other solution (not counting mirror images) if we cut on the dotted lines. If we are allowed to cut wherever we please, there are infinitely many other solutions. Two examples are shown in Figures B and C.

48

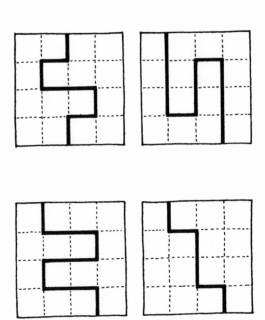

49

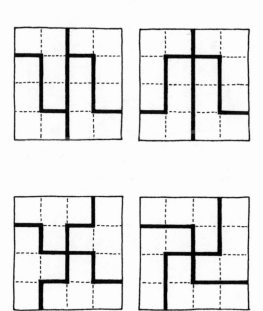

50

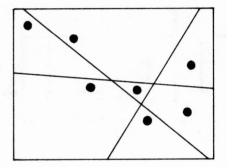

51

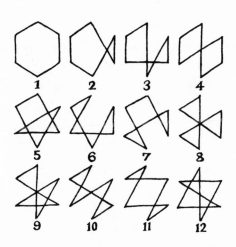

As the illustration shows, there are twelve different paths. This puzzle originated in Mr. Shigetaro Kobayashi's paper "Connecting the Corners of Polygons."

52

Stand three books together as in the illustration. Page one of volume 1 stands next to volume 2, and the last page of volume 3 is also close to volume 2. The moths have eaten through all 3 centimeters of volume 2, the front cover of volume 1, and the back cover of volume 3—a total of 4 centimeters.

53

The girl needs to remove only three socks. Many people guess as many as twenty-two, which is correct only if she needs to remove a pair of a certain color.

There are many famous Japanese *tanka* poems (each with thirty-one syllables) whose authors are unknown. Often they are excellent poems. There are also many excellent short puzzles whose originators are unknown. This is one example.

54

Surprisingly, Plan B is better.

Plan A ($20 increase every year):

$$\text{First year} \quad 50 + 50 = \$100$$
$$\text{Second year} \quad 60 + 60 = \$120$$

Plan B ($5 increase every half year)

$$\text{First year} \quad \$50 + 55 = \$105$$
$$\text{Second year} \quad 60 + 65 = \$125$$

Plan B pays $5 more every year than does Plan A.

55

Most people answer, "Thirty minutes," but this is wrong. When the chemist starts with one cell, it takes one minute for that cell to become two; after that the process is exactly the same. So the entire process takes fifty-nine minutes.

56

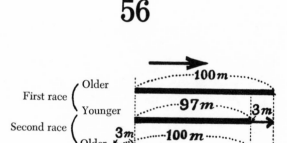

First race ⎰ Older
          ⎱ Younger

Second race ⎰
            ⎱ Older

Finish line

Most people think the result of the second race was a tie, but this is wrong. The younger brother runs 97 meters while his older brother runs 100 meters, so the boys were neck and neck 3 meters short of the finish line. Naturally, the older brother won the second race, too.

57

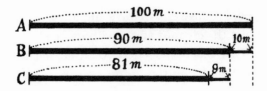

If you said, "A would win by 20 meters," you would be wrong. The difference between the speeds of A and B is 10 percent. There is also a 10 percent difference between B and C. As the illustration shows, if all three ran a race, when A finished, B would trail A by 10 percent of 100, or 10 meters, and C would follow B by 10 percent of 90, or 9 meters. Therefore, if A and C raced each other, A would win by $10 + 9 = 19$ meters.

58

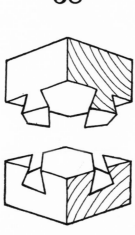

Anyone who sees this puzzling cube for the first time naturally assumes that the lower part must have two grooves that cross at right angles. But as the illustration shows, the two grooves are in fact diagonal to the cubes' sides and parallel to each other. This arrangement permits the parts to slide apart easily.

59

At first this puzzle seems to be extremely difficult, but if you approach it correctly, it is easy. It takes exactly 1 hour for B to catch up with A. Since the dog ran continually during that hour, at 10 km per hour, the dog ran 10 kilometers.

60

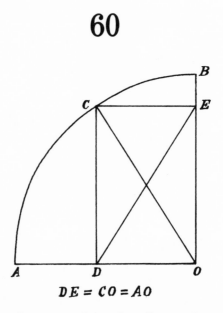

DE = CO = AO

Draw CO, the rectangle's other diagonal. It is obvious that DE = CO. Because CO is a radius of the circular arc, it equals AO. Therefore, DE and AO are the same length.

61

This puzzle is merely a play on words. If you analyze the problem correctly, you will find the right answer.

The 27,000 yen is the sum of the 25,000 that the cashier received and the 2,000 yen that the maid took. Therefore, it does not make sense to add once again the maid's 2,000 yen to the 27,000 yen. It does make sense to add the 3,000 yen that the maid returned, in which case the two amounts equal 30,000 yen.

62

A person's age is indeed unpredictable. The new clerk could be either twenty-two or twenty-four.

63

The answer is of course one centimeter. A puzzle like this is almost too easy and invites error through a hasty response. It is amusing to try this test on friends.

64

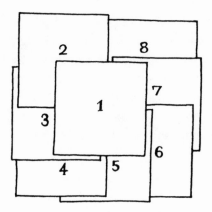

Try other ways of numbering to convince yourself that this is the only correct way.

65

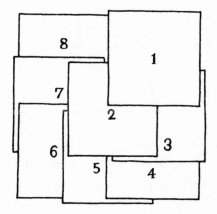

The illustration shows the correct arrangement. It is easy to create puzzles of this type, but you must be careful not to devise one that allows for more than one answer.

66

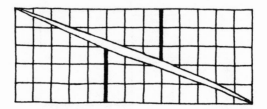

The discrepancy arises because the edges along the diagonal of the second figure do not fit precisely. When you put the four pieces together carefully, so that the borders form an exact rectangle, you leave a gap along the diagonal, as shown. This open area is exactly the size of a small square. Therefore, the area actually covered by the four pieces is still sixty-four small squares.

67

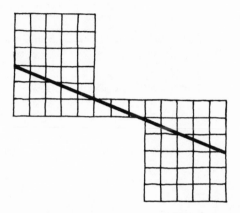

Count the small squares and you will find there are sixty-three. As in the preceding puzzle, this paradox results because edges do not fit perfectly.

The discrepancy of the preceding puzzle was caused by an elongated, parallelogram-shaped hole along the diagonal of a rectangle. In this puzzle, if you put the four parts together precisely, there will be an overlapping of edges along the heavy diagonal line in the picture. The area of this overlap is exactly one small square.

68

	A B C *d e f* *	
1	A B C *d*	*e f* *
2	A B C *d e* *	*f*
3	A B C	*d e f* *
4	A B C *d* *	*e f*
5	A B *d*	C *e f* *
6	A B *d e* *	C *f*
7	A *d e*	B C *f* *
8	A *d e f* *	B C
9	A *d*	B C *e f* *
10	A *d e* *	B C *f*
11	*d e*	A B C *f* *
12	*d e f* *	A B C
13	*f*	A B C *d e* *
14	*e f* *	A B C *d*
15		A B C *def* *

A, B, and C in the chart stand for the three adults and *d, e,* and *f* stand for the three children. The asterisk is the boat. The left side of the chart represents the left bank of the river, where the six persons are standing. The right side of the chart is the other side of the river.

When we begin, all six persons and the boat are on the left. The first move: Since two adults cannot go together, two children, *e* and *f*, cross the river. After that the boat is on the right side. The second move: Leaving *f* on the right bank, *e* returns to the left bank. Now the boat is on the left. The third move: Two children, *d* and *e*, go to the right bank . . .

In this way the fifteenth move completes the crossing of all six persons to the right bank.

69

	A B C *a b c* *	
1	B C *b c*	A *a* *
2	A B C *b c* *	*a*
3	A B C	*a b c* *
4	A B C *a* *	*b c*
5	A *a*	B C *b c* *
6	A B *a b* *	C *c*
7	*a b*	A B C *c* *
8	*a b c* *	A B C
9	*c*	A B C *a b* *
10	C *c* *	A B *a b*
11		A B C *a b c* *

As the chart shows, the six persons crossed the river in eleven moves.

70

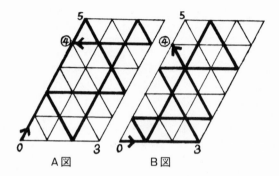

We can solve this problem through a clever method that uses isometric graph paper—paper with a lattice of equilateral triangles. Draw two rhomboids, each with sides of 3 and 5 as shown. The sides correspond to the amount of liters held by the two cans.

By starting at o, we can trace two different paths along the lattice lines, as shown in the two graphs. One path starts by moving up, the other by moving right. In both cases, we end the path when it strikes the longer edge of the rhomboid at the 4 mark.

Each path shows how to solve the problem by pouring water back and forth between the two containers. In Figure A, we start with a filled 5-liter can and an empty 3-liter can. The second line of the path hits the right edge of the rhomboid at a spot that is 3 on the horizontal edge (which represents the 3-liter can) and 2 on the vertical edge (which represents the 5-liter can). This tells us to pour water from the large can into the small one so that the small can contains 3 liters and the large can holds 2 liters.

The path next goes to the left edge of the rhomboid, ending at a spot that is 2 on the large can, 0 on the small can. This tells us to empty the small can, leaving 2 liters in the large can.

The fourth segment of the path tells us to transfer the 2 liters from the large can to the small.

Fifth segment: Leave 2 liters in the small can, fill the large can.

Sixth segment: Fill the small can by pouring from the large. The small can is now filled with 3 liters, and the large can contains 4 liters.

Seventh segment: Empty the small can.

We have 4 liters of water in the large can, so we have solved the problem in seven steps, or five steps if we do not count the initial filling of the large can, or the final emptying of the small can.

Figure B shows a second solution that starts with only the 3-liter can filled. However, this requires one more step than the other method.

This graph method can be used to find the shortest solution for any pouring problem of this type that involves two containers.

71

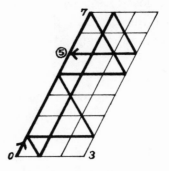

The graph method solves the task in nine operations.

73

There are two methods, A and B, of obtaining 8 pints. In the chart for each method, a row represents one operation.

Method A begins with the 16-pint container filled. Transfer 15 pints to the 15-pint container, leaving 1 pint in the 16-pint container. Then pour out the 15 pints, transfer the remaining pint to the 15-pint container, and fill the 16-pint container again. Fill the 15-pint container with 14 pints from the 16-pint container, pour out the 15 pints, and transfer the remaining 2 pints to the 15-pint container. The same operation is repeated over and over until 8 pints are obtained with step 33.

Method B, which starts with the 15-pint container filled, obtains 8 pints in only 28 steps through the same procedure, so it is the better answer.

A 15	16			B 15	16		
0	16	15	5	15	0	0	11
15	1	0	5	0	15	15	11
0	1	5	0	15	15	10	16
1	0	5	16	14	16	10	0
1	16	15	6	14	0	0	10
15	2	0	6	0	14	15	10
0	2	6	0	15	14	9	16
2	0	6	16	13	16	9	0
2	16	15	7	13	0	0	9
15	3	0	7	0	13	15	9
0	3	7	0	15	10	8	16
3	0	7	16	12	16		
3	16	15	8	12	0		
15	4	0	8	0	12		
0	4	8	0	15	12		
4	0	8	16	11	16		
4	16			11	0		

74

The explanation is simple. Only if the number of apples sold at a penny for 3 apples and the number sold at a penny for 2 are in the ratio of 3:2 will the two ways of selling the apples produce the same result. For example, if one woman turned over to her friend 36 apples, and the other woman gave him 24 apples, the payments would amount to 24 pennies. It would not make any difference whether the apples were sold separately at the original costs or whether they were lumped together and sold at 5 for two pennies.

However, since the two women had the same number of apples left over, they lost a penny when the 60 apples were sold. If they had been left with 60 apples each, their loss would have been two pennies, and if left with 90 each, they would have lost three pennies.

One penny seemed to vanish because the woman who sold 3 apples for a penny made a profit of two pennies and the other woman, who sold 2 apples for a penny, lost three pennies. The difference is the missing penny. A fair division of the 24 pennies would be 9½ pennies for the first woman and 14½ pennies for the second woman. Thus, each woman lost half a penny by changing her selling price.

75

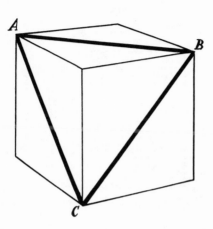

Did you wrongly guess 45°? As the picture shows, drawing a third diagonal, AC, completes an equilateral triangle. The correct answer, therefore, is 60°.

76

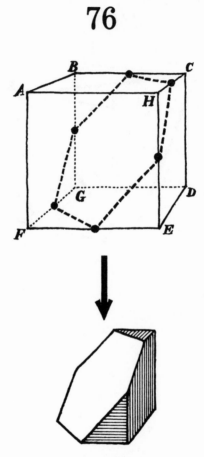

Mark halfway points on edges BC, CH, HF, EF, FG, and GB. Push the knife downward on a slant from the top and cut along the dotted lines. The two new surfaces will be regular hexagons. One of the two identical pieces of cheese is shown in the lower illustration.

77

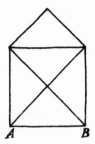

Leonhard Euler, a famous Swiss mathematician of the eighteenth century, proved the following rules for tracing figures:

1. If an even number of lines meet at every point, you can start tracing at any point and complete the drawing in one path.

2. If an odd number of lines meet at two points and an even number at all other points, you can start at either of the odd points and draw a continuous path that must end at the other odd point.

3. If there are four odd points, you can draw the picture in two separate strokes. If there are six odd points, you can draw it in three strokes. In general, if there are $2n$ odd points, you can draw a figure in n paths.

In our problem the lower left and right corners of the two TV screens are the only odd points. To draw the picture in one path you must start at one of these corners and finish at the other.

78

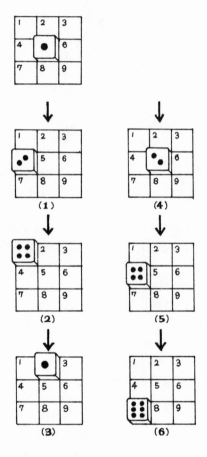

Six moves will solve the puzzle: 5 – 4 – 1 – 2 – 5 – 4 – 7.

From the initial position you can roll the die so that it ends on any square with any face on top. You may enjoy ways of solving other such problems.

79

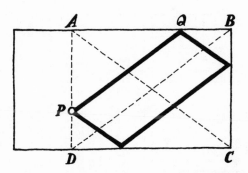

First, draw a line through P that is parallel to side BC. This creates the rectangle ABCD. Draw diagonal lines AC and BD. Now draw a line through P that is parallel to BD. It will intersect AB at Q, the point you wish to find.

80

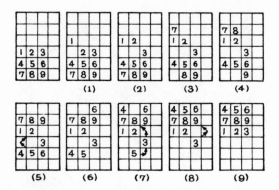

(1) (2) (3) (4)

(5) (6) (7) (8) (9)

You might say offhand that the transfer would take ten or eleven moves. The truth is that it can be done in nine.

In the illustration above I have used numbers for the chips to identify each and trace its movement.

The six-by-four array of squares is necessary to make the eighth move. Without the extra column, chip 5 could not be moved upward.

81

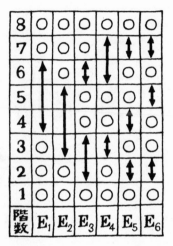

Six elevators will do it. The illustration shows how.

82

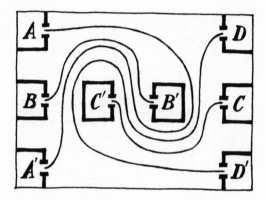

This is one way to do it; there are others.

83

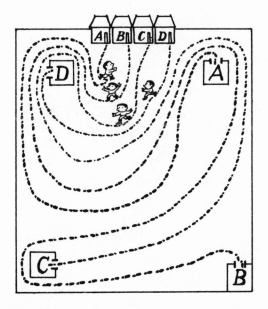

The illustration gives one answer.

84

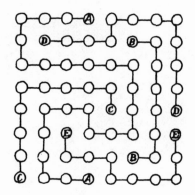

85

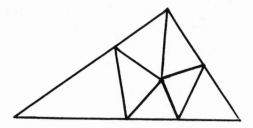

The triangle can be divided into as few as seven acute triangles.

86

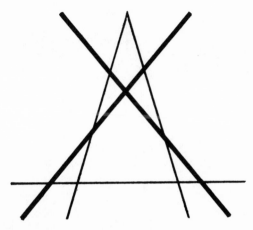

Adding two lines as shown produces ten triangles; four small ones, two larger ones, and four very large ones.

87

88

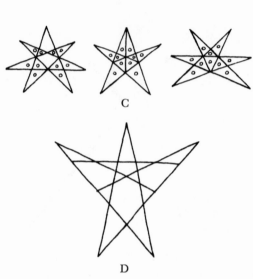

For many years it was thought that no more than ten nonoverlapping triangles could be made with seven straight lines, but it is possible to make eleven! Figure D shows how.

89

If we open all the links in the 8-link piece it will cost 80 yen. For 160 yen these links can be closed to join the 8 other pieces into one ring. The total expense will be 240 yen.

There is an even less expensive way, however! Open all the links of the 3-ring and 4-ring pieces. This will cost 70 yen. With those 7 links, join the remaining 7 pieces, at a cost of only 140 yen. The total will be 210 yen, or 40 yen less than the price of a new chain.

90

You may have reasoned: "From twenty-four I must subtract two, since the long hand did not pass the short hand at either the start or finish of twenty-four hours." But 22 is *not* the correct answer! The right answer is 21. If you doubt this, try it with your watch. You will see that the long hand passes the short hand only *once* between eleven o'clock and one.

91

	A	B	C	D	E
A		×	×	×	×
B	○		○	○	×
C	○	×		○	×
D	○	×	×		×
E	○	○	○	○	

The formula for the number of games is $\dfrac{n\,(n-1)}{2}$ where n = number of teams. Therefore, the number of games played was 10.

92

Statements (3) and (5) suggest the situation in Chart 1, below.

Facing each other		
Archaeologist		
Essayist	B	Musician

When we incorporate statement (8), that D is sitting opposite the novelist, we get the two possibilities shown in charts 2A and 2B below:

Chart 2A

Archaeologist	D	
Essayist	B Novelist	Musician

Chart 2B

Archaeologist		Novelist
Essayist	B	D Musician

Look at Chart 2A. On the basis of statement (4), we must put E either in the top right-hand corner or upper left-hand corner. However, in either case it contradicts (6). Hence, we discard Chart 2A and take Chart 2B. This leads to the two possibilities shown in charts 3A and 3B:

Chart 3A

Archaeologist		Novelist
E Essayist	B Playwright	D Musician

Chart 3B

E Archaeologist	Playwright	Novelist
Essayist	B	D Musician

In each of the above charts, we place A on the basis of 1 and 7. This gives us charts 4A and 4B:

Chart 4A

Archaeologist		A Novelist
E Essayist	B Playwright	D Musician

Chart 4B

E Archaeologist	Playwright	A Novelist
Essayist	B	D Musician

Let's study Chart 4A. From 10 we deduce that C is the poet. However, if we place C in the center of the top line, it contradicts 6, because according to 2, C then must be reading a book written by the playwright. Therefore, we must give up Chart 4A and take 4B. This confirms that B is the poet and it justifies the final chart 5:

Chart 5

E Archaeologist	Playwright	A Novelist
Essayist	B Poet	D Musician

This establishes that the playwright is either F or C. If we assume the playwright is F, the essayist must be C. Then it follows that C is reading a book on archaeology as (2) states. In addition, E is reading a book on music (statement 9); D is reading the playwright's book (state-

ment 6); A is reading the essays (statement 1). Consequently, B, the poet, must be reading the novel and F is
reading poems. However, this contradicts statement 10.
Therefore, our assumption is wrong. The playwright must
be C and F must be the essayist.

We have finally arrived at a consistent answer:

A novelist
B poet
C playwright
D musician
E archaeologist
F essayist

Note that E and A are interchangeable, and so are F
and D. You can also get the right answer if you put them
on the other side, facing the other way. In other words,
you cannot pin down exactly in which seat each man
must sit.

93

The students, from highest to lowest, rank as follows:

F
A & B
C
E
D

94

A bought shoes on the first floor.
B bought a book on the third floor.
C bought a camera on the second floor.
D bought a watch on the fourth floor.

95

First, let us find the missing age in the group. The sum of numbers 1 through 13 is 91. The grand total of the children's ages in the three families is 84. Therefore, the missing age is 7.

Now, let us answer the two questions: The 4 children in Family A can be either 12, 6, 10, 13 or 12, 8, 10, 11 (12 must be included). The 4 children in Family C can be 4, 1, 3, 13 or 4, 1, 6, 10 or 4, 2, 6, 9 or 4, 3, 6, 8 (4 must be included). Then Family A must be 12, 8, 10, 11. Family C is 4, 1, 3, 13 or 4, 2, 6, 9. (Remember that Family C has no children born one year apart.)

Therefore, Family C must be 4, 2, 6, 9. Family B must be 5, 1, 3, 13. I am one of the children in Family B.

96

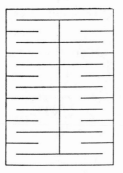

The narrower the distance between the cut lines, the larger the ring. Try it and you'll be astonished by how large a ring you can get.

97

1. E pushes B into the tunnel.
2. E goes around the loop and pushes A down until it meets B and joins all three cars.
3. E pushes B and A around the loop, past the switch, and then backs up and leaves B where E was at the start.
4. E pushes A back to its starting position.
5. E pulls B into the loop, then pushes it up and around to meet A.

6. E pushes both cars until A is in the tunnel.
7. Leaving A, E pulls B and leaves it at the spot where A was at the start.
8. E continues alone around the loop until it meets A.
9. E pulls A from the tunnel and leaves it where B was at the start.
10. E returns to its original position.

98

After the first day, A set aside one day's food for himself and gave the remaining food (three days' portion) to B, C, and D.

The next morning, A returned to the base alone. B, C, and D advanced. After the second day, B set aside two days' food for himself and gave the rest (two days' portion) to C and D.

After the third day, C set aside three days' food for his return trip and gave the rest (one day's portion) to D. Thus, D advanced until the end of the fourth day, after which he had just enough to return to the base.